It's Easy To Play Love Songs.

Wise Publications
London / New York / Paris / Sydney / Copenhagen / Madrid

Exclusive Distributors:

Music Sales Limited
8/9 Frith Street, London W1V 5TZ, England.

Music Sales Pty Limited
120 Rothschild Avenue, Rosebery, NSW 2018, Australia.

Order No. AM956220
ISBN 0-7119-7941-3
This book © Copyright 1999 by Wise Publications.

Cover photographs courtesy of London Features International,
Retna, Rex Features London and SuperStock.
Compiled by Peter Evans.
Music arranged by Stephen Duro.
Music processed by Allegro Reproductions.

Music Sales' complete catalogue describes thousands of titles and
is available in full colour sections by subject, direct from Music Sales Limited.
Please state your areas of interest and send a cheque/postal order for £1.50 for postage to:
Music Sales Limited, Newmarket Road, Bury St. Edmunds, Suffolk IP33 3YB.

www.musicsales.co.uk

Your Guarantee of Quality:
As publishers, we strive to produce every book to the highest commercial standards.
The music has been freshly engraved and the book has been carefully designed to minimise awkward page turns and to make playing from it a real pleasure.
Particular care has been given to specifying acid-free, neutral-sized paper made from pulps which have not been elemental chlorine bleached.
This pulp is from farmed sustainable forests and was produced with special regard for the environment.
Throughout, the printing and binding have been planned to ensure a sturdy, attractive publication which should give years of enjoyment.
If your copy fails to meet our high standards, please inform us and we will gladly replace it.

Printed in the United Kingdom by
Caligraving Limited, Thetford, Norfolk.

And I Love Her

Words & Music by John Lennon & Paul McCartney

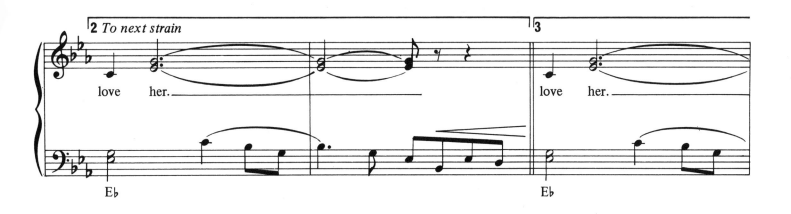

love her. _____ love her. _____

E♭   E♭

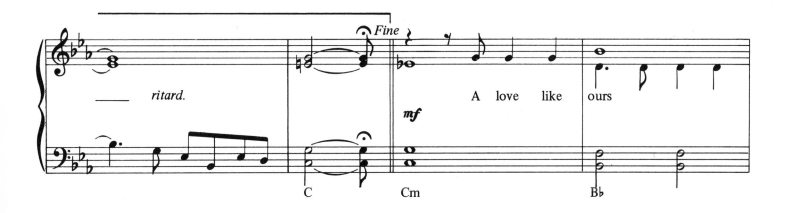

_____ *ritard.*   A love like ours

mf

C   Cm   B♭

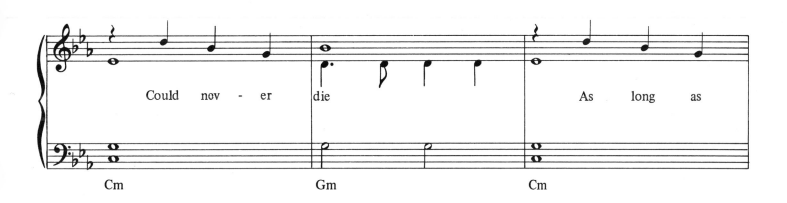

Could nev - er die   As long as

Cm   Gm   Cm

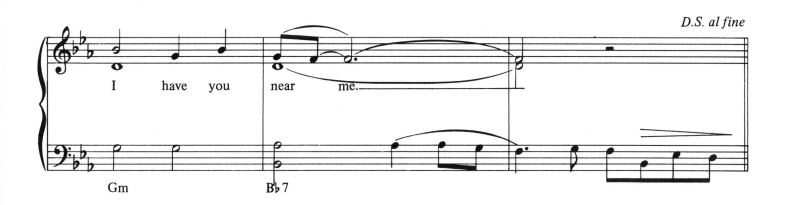

D.S. al fine

I have you near me. _____

Gm   B♭7

Falling Into You

Words & Music by Rick Nowels, Marie-Claire D'Ubaldo & Billy Steinberg

7

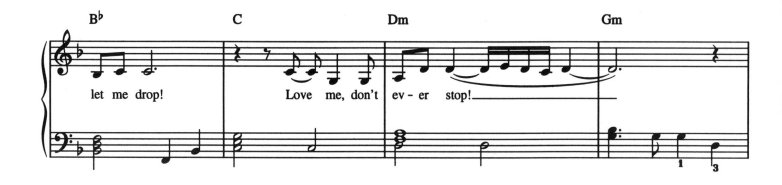

let me drop!   Love me, don't ev - er stop!____

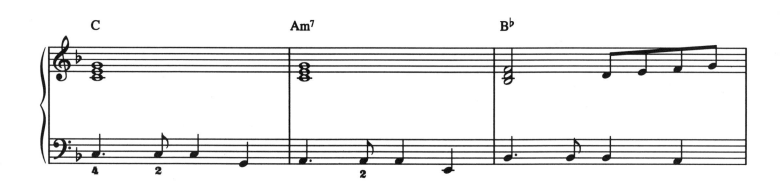

3. So close your

eyes   and let____ me kiss you.____   And while

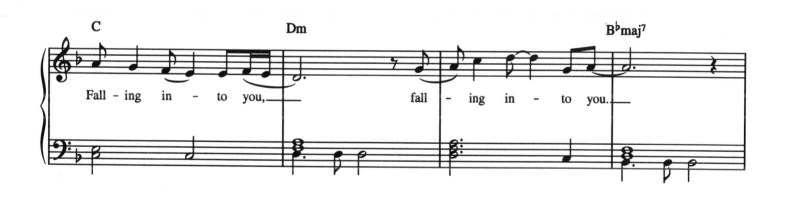

9

Have I Told You Lately

Words & Music by Van Morrison

There's a love that's di-vine And it's yours and it's mine,— like the

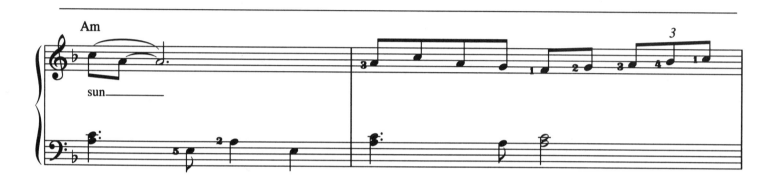

sun——

At the end of the day—— We should give thanks and pray to the

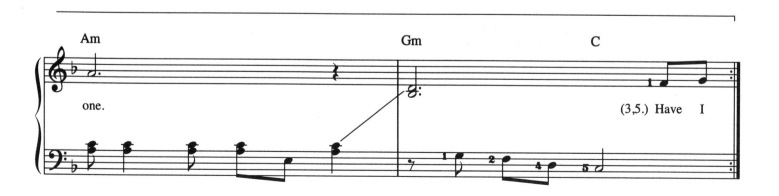

one. (3,5.) Have I

do.   Fill my heart with glad - ness,

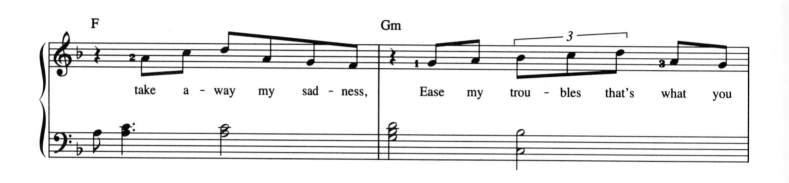

take a - way my sad - ness, Ease my trou - bles that's what you

do.   do.

Verse 2:

Oh the morning sun in all its glory
Greets the day with hope and comfort too
And you fill my life with laughter
You can make it better
Ease my troubles that's what you do.

Verse 3: - as Verse 1

Verse 4: - Instrumental

Middle:

There's a love that's divine
And it's yours and its mine
And it shines like the sun
At the end of the day
We will give thanks and pray to the one.

Verse 5: - as Verse 1

How Deep Is Your Love

Words & Music by Barry Gibb, Robin Gibb & Maurice Gibb

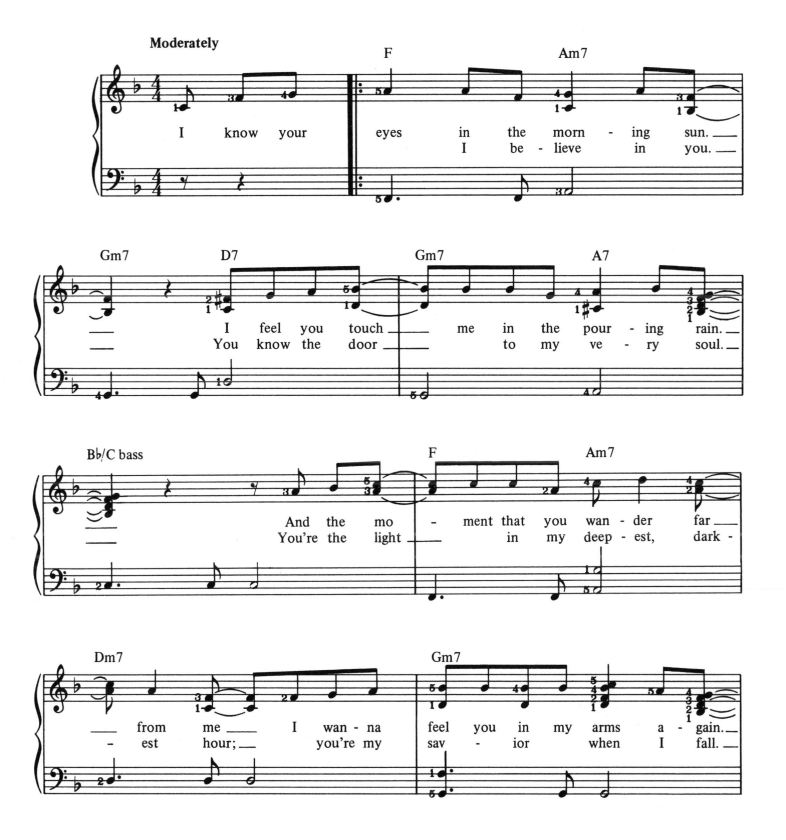

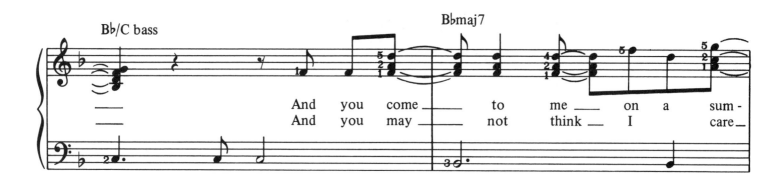

And you come ____ to me ____ on a sum-
And you may ____ not think ____ I care

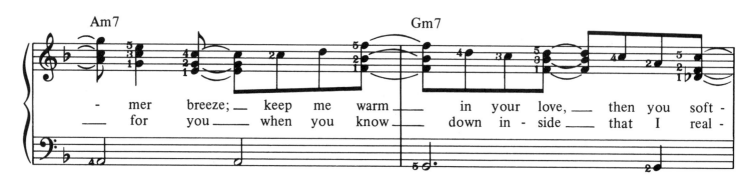

- mer breeze; ____ keep me warm ____ in your love, ____ then you soft-
- for you ____ when you know ____ down in-side ____ that I real-

- ly leave. ____ And it's me you need ____ to show: ____
- ly do. ____

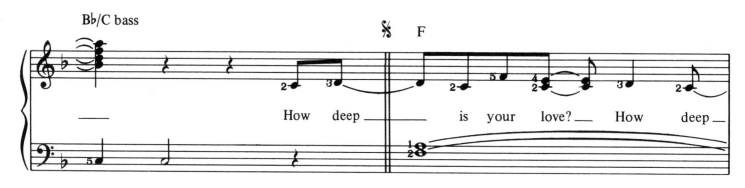

How deep ____ is your love? ____ How deep ____

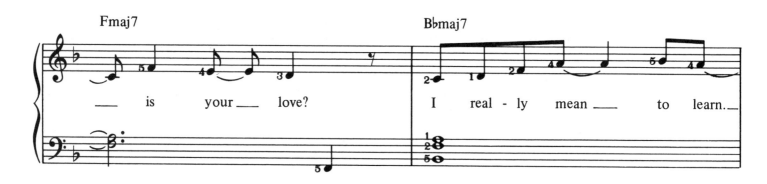

____ is your ____ love? I real-ly mean ____ to learn. ____

Just The Two Of Us

Words & Music by Ralph MacDonald, William Salter & Bill Withers

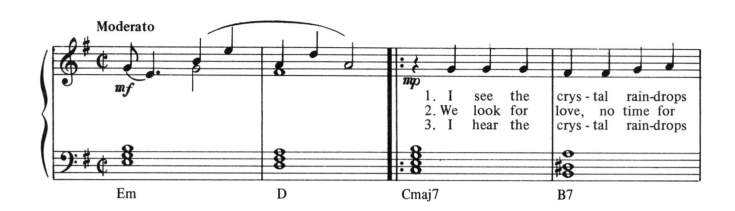

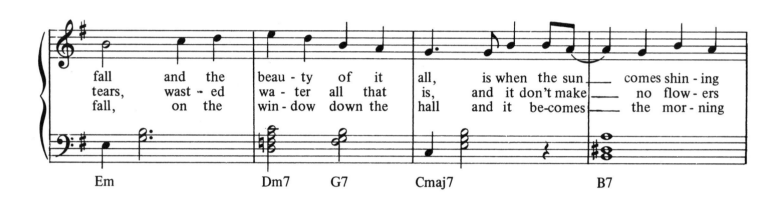

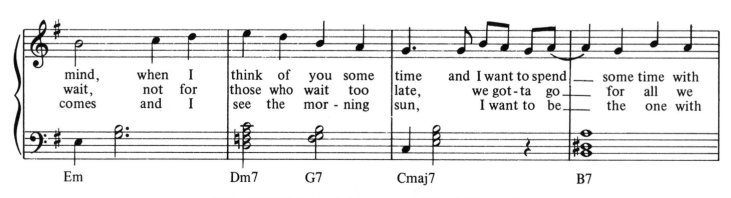

I Just Called To Say I Love You

Words & Music by Stevie Wonder

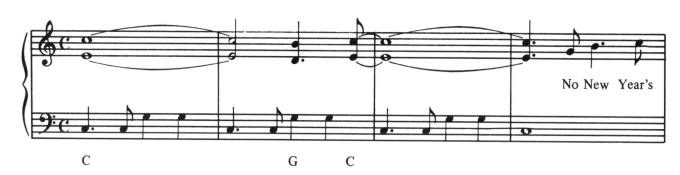

No New Year's

C   G   C

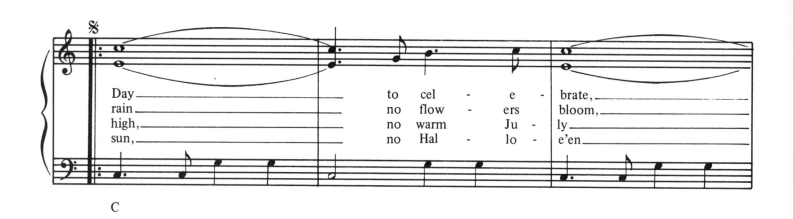

Day		to cel - e	brate,
rain		no flow - ers	bloom,
high,		no warm Ju -	ly
sun,		no Hal - lo -	e'en

C

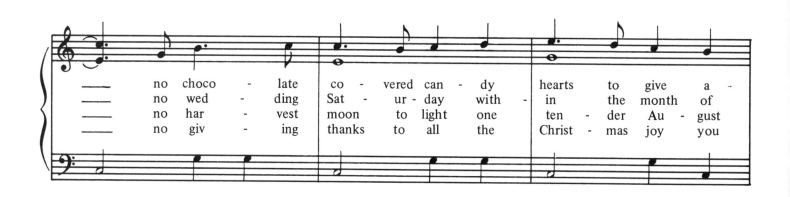

no choco - late	co - vered can - dy	hearts to give a -
no wed - ding	Sat - ur - day with -	in the month of
no har - vest	moon to light one	ten - der Au - gust
no giv - ing	thanks to all the	Christ - mas joy you

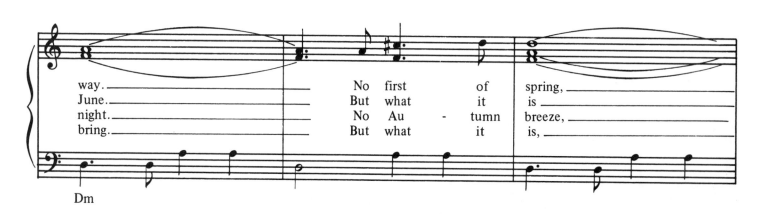

way.	No first of	spring,
June.	But what it	is
night.	No Au - tumn	breeze,
bring.	But what it	is,

Dm

no song to sing, _____ in fact here's
is some - thing true, _____ made up of
no fall - ing leaves, _____ not ev - en
though old so new, _____ to fill your

just an - oth - er or - din - ar - y day. _____
these three words that I must say to
time for birds to fly to south - ern
heart like no three words could ev - er

Dm7   C/G   G   C

1

2, 4

— no A - pril
you. _____
do. _____   I just called _____ to

C   Dm

say I love ____ you, _____ I just called _____ to

G   C   Dm

say how much I care. _____ I just called _____ to

G   Am   Dm

Love Is All Around

Words & Music by Reg Presley

Verse 2:

I see your face before me
As I lay on my bed;
I cannot get to thinking
Of all the things you said.
You gave your promise to me
And I gave mine to you;
I need someone beside me
In everything I do.

Something

Words & Music by George Harrison

1. You're ask - ing me, will my love grow?
2. You stick a - round, now it may show.

I don't know; I don't know. I don't know.

Some-thing in the way she knows and all I have to do is think of her. some-thing in the way she shows me. I don't want to leave her now, you know I be-lieve and how *ritard.*

(A)   Amaj7   F#m   A

D   G   A7

C   (C)   Cmaj7

C7   F   D7   G

Am   Am7   D7   F   Eb G7   C

She

Words by Herbert Kretzmer
Music by Charles Aznavour

Moderately slow

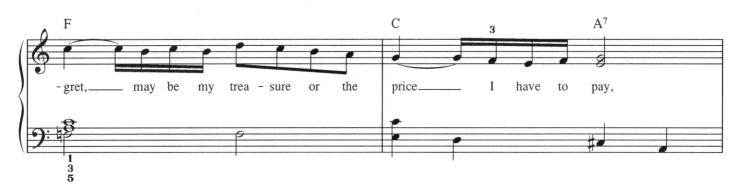

1. She___ may be the face I can't for – get,___ a trace of plea - sure or re –

- gret,___ may be my trea - sure or the price___ I have to pay,

she___ may be the song that sum - mer sings,___ may be the chill that au - tumn

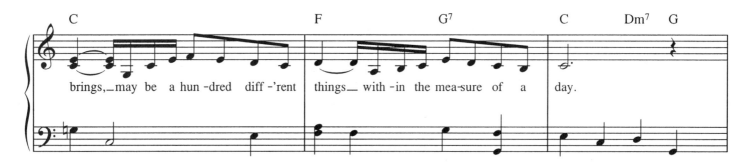

brings,___may be a hun -dred diff -'rent things___ with -in the mea-sure of a day.

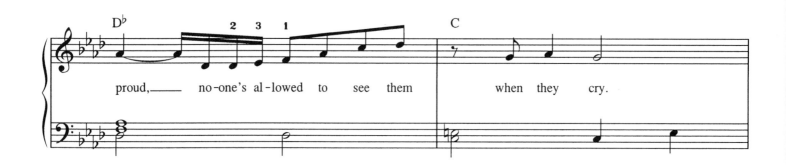

proud,___ no-one's al-lowed to see them when they cry.

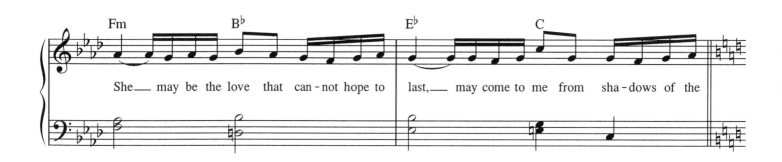

She___ may be the love that can-not hope to last,___ may come to me from sha-dows of the

past___ that I'll re-mem-ber till the day I die.

D.S. al Coda

CODA

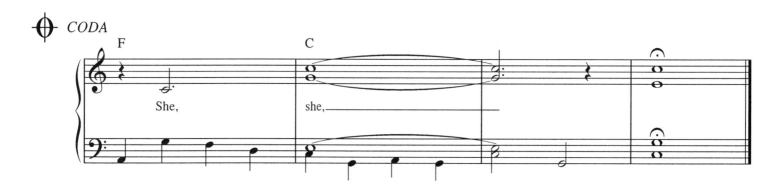

She, she,___

Verse 4:

She may be the reason I survive
The why and wherefore I'm alive
The one I'll care for through the rough and ready years.
Me, I'll take her laughter and her tears
And make them all my souvenirs
For where she goes I've got to be
The meaning of my life is she, she, she.

Take My Breath Away

Words by Tom Whitlock
Music by Giorgio Moroder

This Guy's In Love With You

Words by Hal David
Music by Burt Bacharach

33

Unchained Melody

Words by Hy Zaret
Music by Alex North

To Coda ⊕

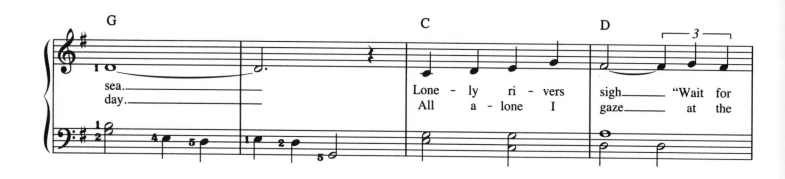

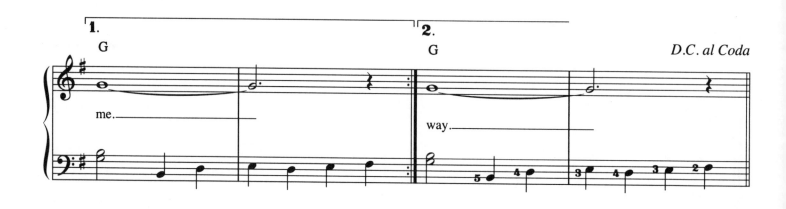

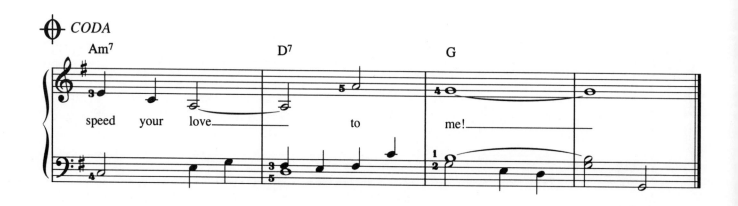

When You Tell Me
That You Love Me

Words & Music by Albert Hammond & John Bettis

Moderately

I wan-na call the stars down from the sky, I wan-na live a day that ne-ver dies. I wan-na change the world on-ly for you, all the im-pos-si-ble I wan-na do. I wan-na

hold you close un-der the rain, I wan-na kiss your smile and feel your
make you see just what I was, show you the lone-li-ness and what it

We've Only Just Begun

Words by Paul Williams
Music by Roger Nichols

We start out walk-ing and learn to run. ⎱
We'll find a place where there's room to grow. ⎰ And yes, we've just be-gun. _____

Dm   Gm7   Fmaj7   B♭

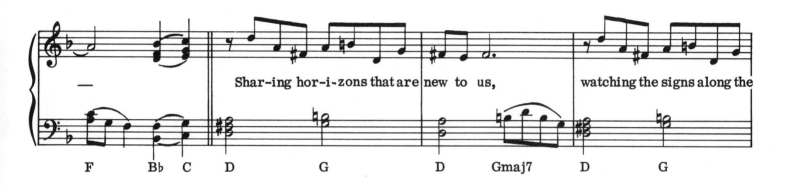

_____ Shar-ing hor-i-zons that are new to us,   watching the signs along the

F   B♭   C   D   G   D   Gmaj7   D   G

way.   Talk-ing it ov-er just the two of us,   working to-geth-er, day to

D   Gmaj7   F♯   B   F♯   Bmaj7   F♯   B

1
day,   to - geth - er. _____

2   *D.S. al Coda* 𝄋
geth-er, _____ to - geth-er. _____

Gm7   (Gm7)   Gm7

⊕ **CODA**

_____ And yes, we've just be - gun. _____

Gm7   Fmaj7   Gm7   Fmaj7

What Can I Do

Words & Music by Andrea Corr, Caroline Corr, Sharon Corr & Jim Corr

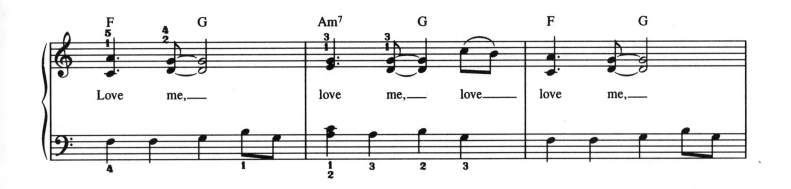

Love me,   love me,   love   love me,

love me,   love,   love me,   love me,   love,

love me,   love me,   love,   love   me.

Verse 2:

There's only so much I can take
And I just got to let it go
And who knows I might feel better
If I don't try and I don't hope.

What can I do...

Words

Words & Music by Barry Gibb, Robin Gibb & Maurice Gibb

Moderately

Smile an ev-er-last-ing smile; a smile could bring you near to me.

Don't ev-er let me find you gone 'cause that would bring a

tear to me. This world has lost its glo-ry;

let's start a brand new sto-ry now, my love. Right

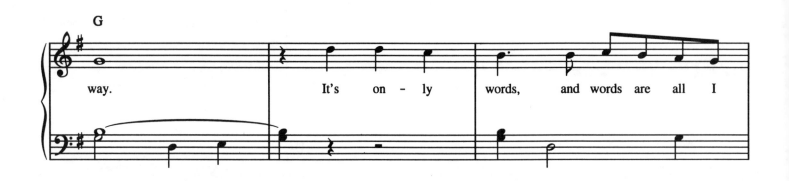

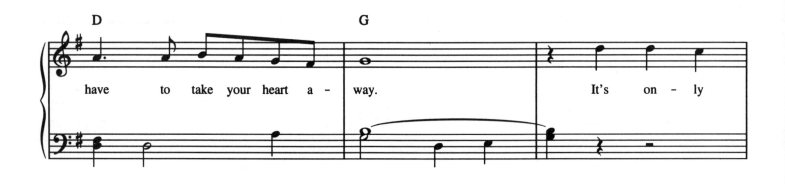